Dedicated to all the women currently navigating
their way through the menopause.

For my Mum,
love Jen x

To all the special ladies in my life;
young, old and in-between,
love Charlie x

# MARTHA GETS THE MENOPAUSE

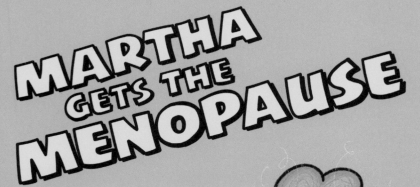

Jennifer Kennedy
and
Charlie Fowkes

During the menopause, Martha became invisible to society. However, this made shop-lifting easier.

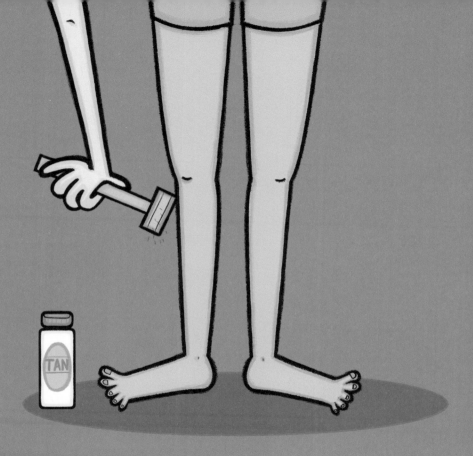

Before the menopause, Martha used to shave or wax her legs and lady garden every day.

During the menopause, Martha's leg and lady hairs disappeared, which was great as it gave her time and money to focus on her newly sprouting facial hair.

During the menopause, Martha pissed herself at trampoline class and went to work in her slippers.

Before the menopause, Martha decided she would approach it in a natural way.

During the menopause, Martha would try anything, legal or otherwise, to deal with it.

Before the menopause, Martha was a successful business woman whose career was on an upward trajectory.

During the menopause, Martha started telling her colleagues to 'feck off' and couldn't remember anything, so had to leave before they sacked her.

Before the menopause, Martha liked to work out.

During the menopause, Martha couldn't be bothered and just lay on the sofa drinking multiple gins and eating chocolate.

Before the menopause, Martha was a supermum who would do anything for her kids including visiting multiple supermarkets to get the freshest ingredients for healthy meals.

During the menopause, Martha could not give a shit what the kids ate or did.

Before the menopause, Martha had a rich vocabulary.

Before the menopause, Martha had a great sex life.

During the menopause, Martha preferred a mint ice cream while watching a box set.

Before the menopause, Martha had a fabulous social life with regular nights out.

During the menopause, Martha's favourite plans were cancelled plans.

Before the menopause, Martha had a small, sensible, run-into-the-ground type car that suited the needs of her family.

Since the menopause, Martha drives a sexy, impractical, bright purple convertible she had always wanted and makes the kids get the bus.

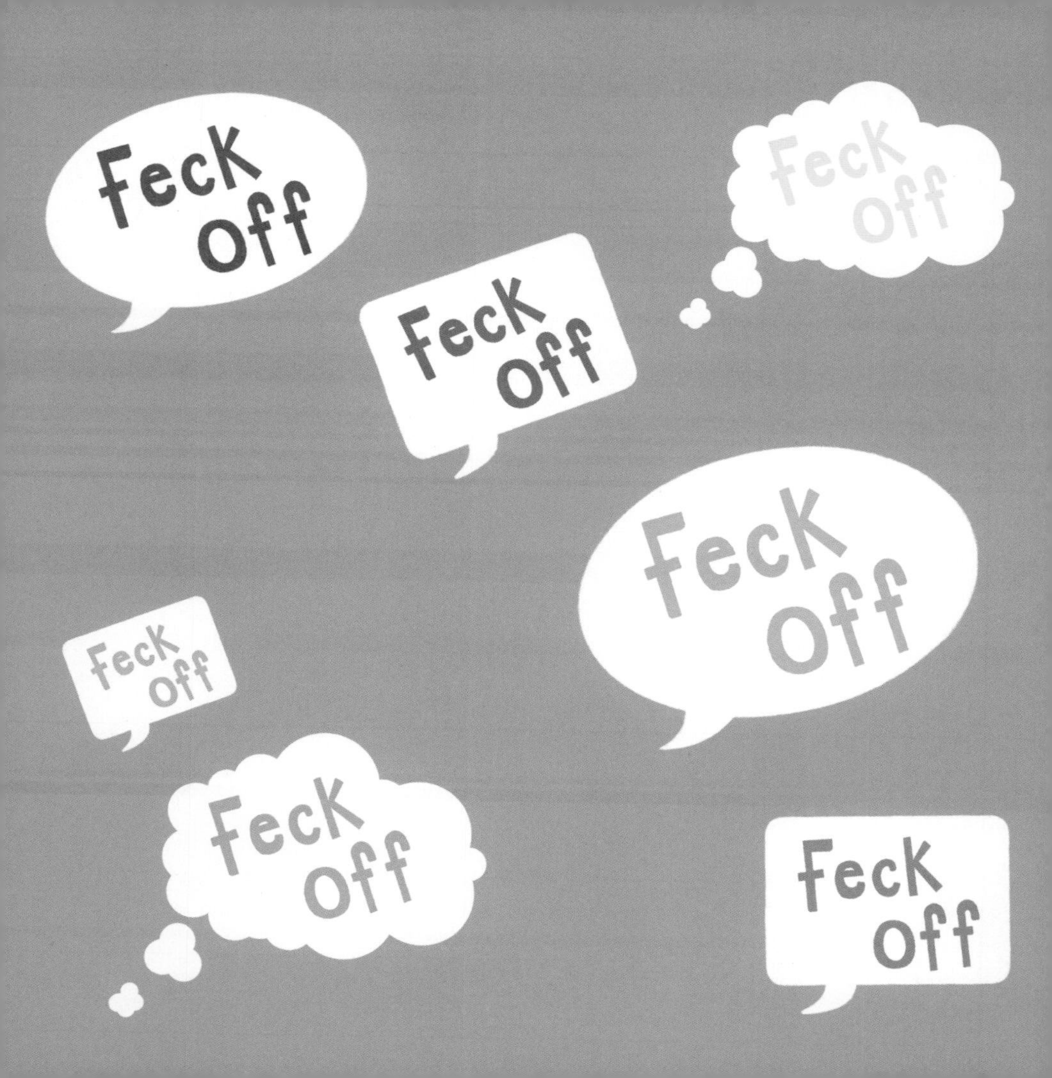
Feck Off
Feck Off
Feck Off
Feck Off
Feck Off
Feck Off
Feck Off